KEVIN HATHWAY & IAN WRI

Graded Music for Tuned Percussion

Book IV

These pieces have been arranged by Kevin Hathway & Ian Wright

Accompaniments by Kreisler[1], Emma Parsons[2] & Gordon Lewin[3]

THE ASSOCIATED BOARD OF
THE ROYAL SCHOOLS OF MUSIC

Graded Music for Tuned Percussion, Book IV
Presto
from Concerto in A minor, Op.3 No.6

VIVALDI

AB 2146

2

4

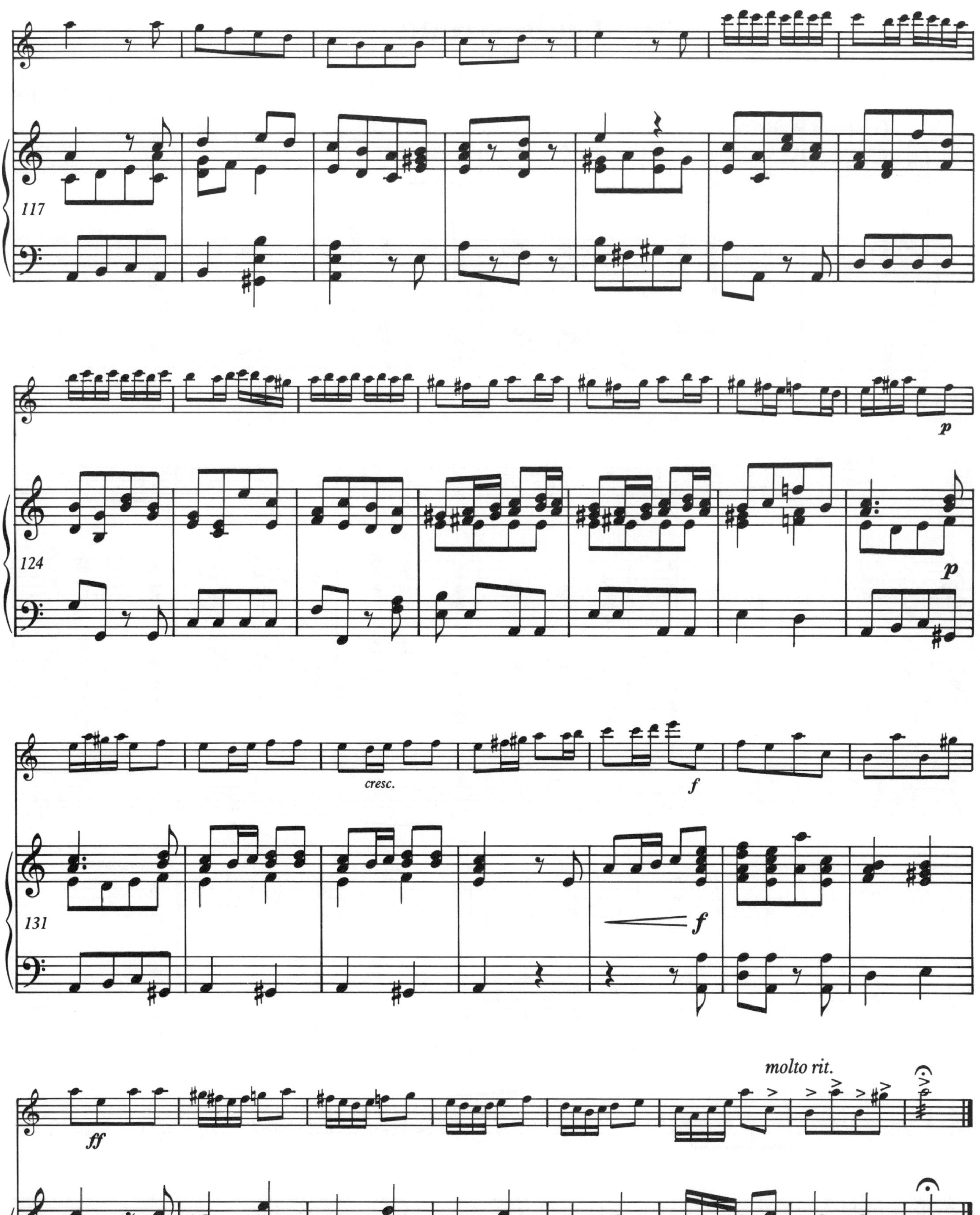
117
p
124
p
cresc.
f
131
f
molto rit.
ff
138
ff

Liebesfreud

KREISLER

Alla Turca

from Sonata in A, K.331

MOZART

12

AB 2146

14

Black and White Rag

GEORGE BOTSFORD

D.S. al 𝄋 poi alla Coda

CODA

GRADE 7

Sight Reading Examples

BEETHOVEN

SCHUMANN

D.C. al Fine

AB 2146

Allegro

from Sonata in E, Op.1 No.15

HANDEL

Bourrée anglaise

from Sonata in A minor for unaccompanied flute, BWV 1013

J.S. BACH

6

Presto

from Concerto in A minor, Op.3 No.6

VIVALDI

8

Asturias

from *Suite Española*

ALBÉNIZ

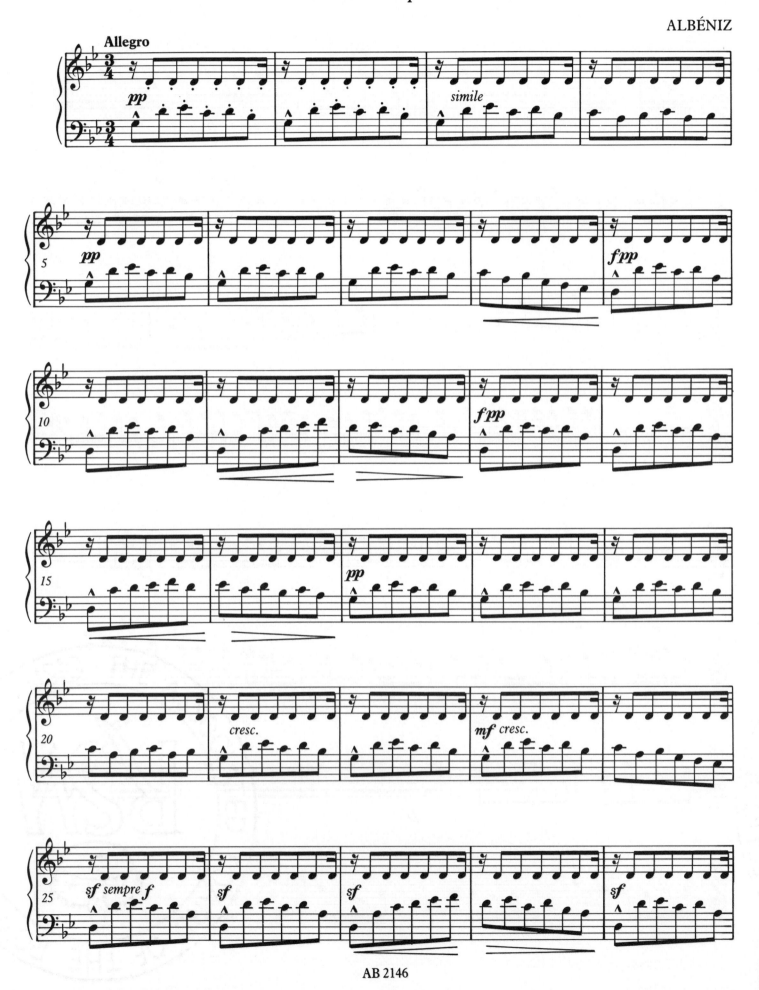

Thunder and Lightning Polka

JOHANN STRAUSS Op.324

Liebesfreud

KREISLER

AB 2146

The Favorite and Ragtime Two Step

JOPLIN

GRADE 8

Sight Reading Examples

AB 2146

Allegro

from Concerto in A minor, Op.3 No.6

VIVALDI

Gigue

from Violin Partita No.2, BWV 1004

J.S. BACH

Alla Turca

from Sonata in A, K.331

MOZART

The Flight of the Bumble Bee

from *The Tale of Tsar Saltan*

RIMSKY-KORSAKOV

Czardas

MONTI

Danse Bohème

from *Carmen*, Act 2

BIZET

Pizzicato Polka

Arranged for 4 mallets
by Kevin Hathway

JOHANN & JOSEF STRAUSS

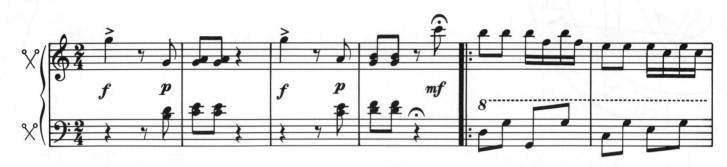

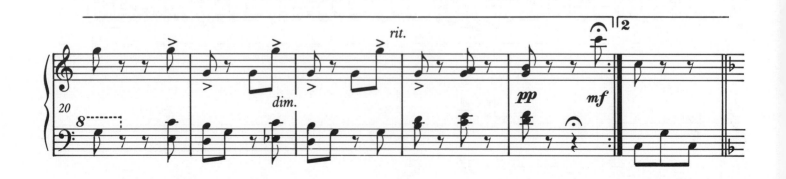

Schön Rosmarin

KREISLER

Black and White Rag

GEORGE BOTSFORD

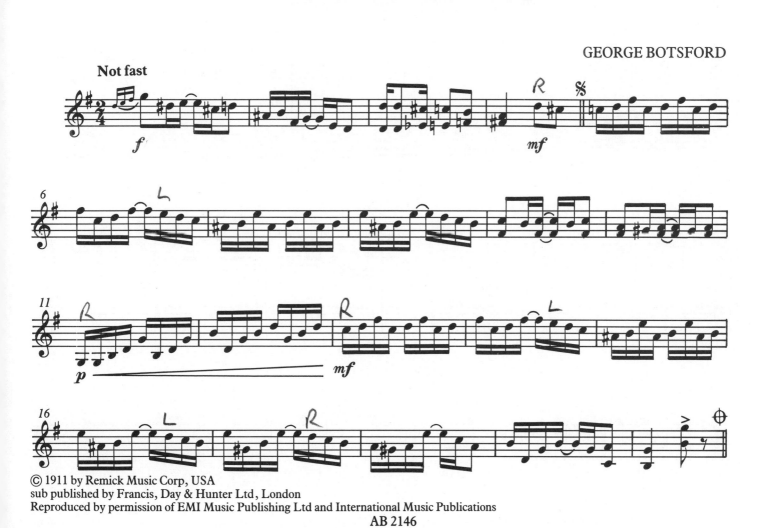

sub published by Francis, Day & Hunter Ltd, London
Reproduced by permission of EMI Music Publishing Ltd and International Music Publications

D.S. al ⊕ poi alla Coda

CODA

♪ = handle on handle

Printed in England by Caligraving Limited Thetford Norfolk

AB 2146